# Stop, Zebra!

Written by Ian MacDonald

Illustrated by Leire Martin

Yasmin has a ticket to go on a visit.

Yasmin and Mum grin at the zebras.

# From the picnic mat they spot the vet.

# The zebra panics and gets in a gap.

The zebra gets her leg stuck in a bucket.

Can I get a snack for the zebra?

The zebra trots to the snack.

# The zebra gets a snack. Yasmin gets tickets!

# Talk about the story

Ask your child these questions:

**1** What did Yasmin and her mum grin at?

**2** How did the zebra get out of his pen?

**3** When did Yasmin spot the vet?

**4** What idea did the vet have to get the zebra back?

**5** What do you think zebras like to eat?

**6** Have you ever been to a zoo or wildlife park?

Can your child retell the story using their own words?